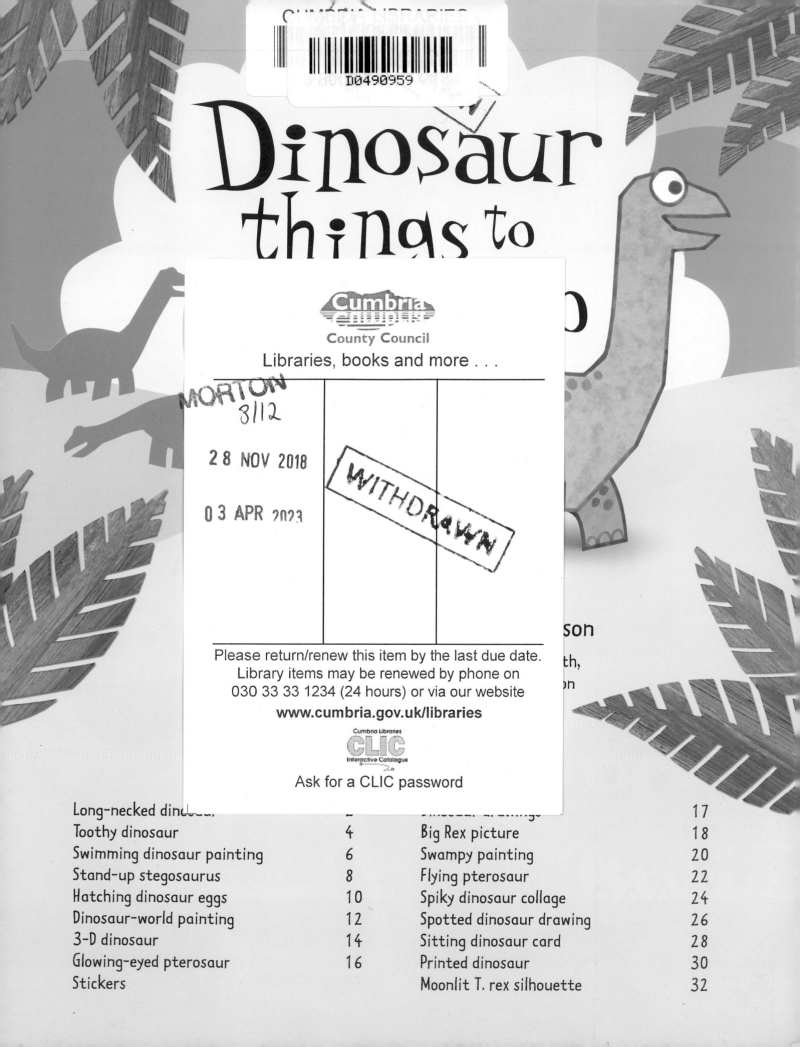

Dinosaur things to do

...son

th,
...on

Long-necked dinosaur

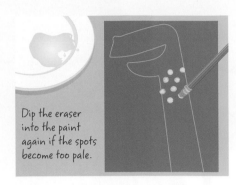

Dip the eraser into the paint again if the spots become too pale.

1. Draw a dinosaur with a long neck and an open mouth on a piece of thick paper. Then, dip the eraser on the end of a pencil into thick paint. Print lots of spots down the neck.

2. Leave the spots to dry completely. Then, cut out the dinosaur and turn it over. Spread glue on the back, then press it onto another piece of paper.

3. Cut two white paper circles for eyes and glue them on. Then, use a black felt-tip pen to draw spots on the eyes for pupils. Draw lots of teeth inside the mouth, too.

4. Using a felt-tip pen, draw lots of spines down the dinosaur's back. Draw two black spots for nostrils, then add a little brown curve for the nose, like this.

You could make a big picture with lots of dinosaurs. Look at the ideas shown here.

To decorate this dinosaur, paint a piece of white paper with watery yellow paint, then dab on runny orange paint.

Spots printed with bubblewrap – see steps 3-5 on pages 30-31.

Use a strip cut from a kitchen sponge to print stripes.

Try printing markings with the end of an eraser.

You could glue leaves cut from green paper around your dinosaurs.

These prints were made with a pencil eraser.

To print scales, cut a scale shape from a sponge cloth and dip it into different shades of paint.

These spots were fingerpainted.

You could paint scales with a thin paintbrush.

Toothy dinosaur

Line up the edges of the shapes.

You will use the pink shape in step 5.

1. Fold a piece of thick yellow paper in half. Using a pencil, draw a rectangle with rounded corners for a dinosaur's head. Then, holding the layers together, cut out the shape.

2. Fold one of the paper shapes in half, then unfold it. Turn it over, then spread glue on the top half, above the fold. Press it onto the top half of the other paper shape.

3. Draw around the dinosaur's head on pieces of pink and orange paper. Cut out both shapes. Then, cut a strip off each side of the orange shape to leave a central stripe.

For a dinosaur like this, draw a circle in step 1, then add triangles at the top and bottom.

You could give a toothy dinosaur to someone as a card — just write a message on the back or inside the mouth.

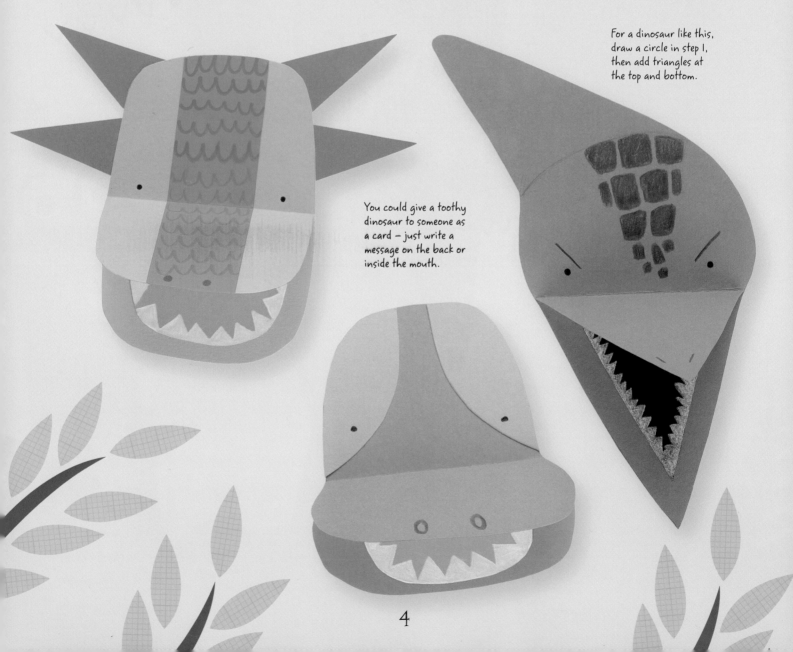

4

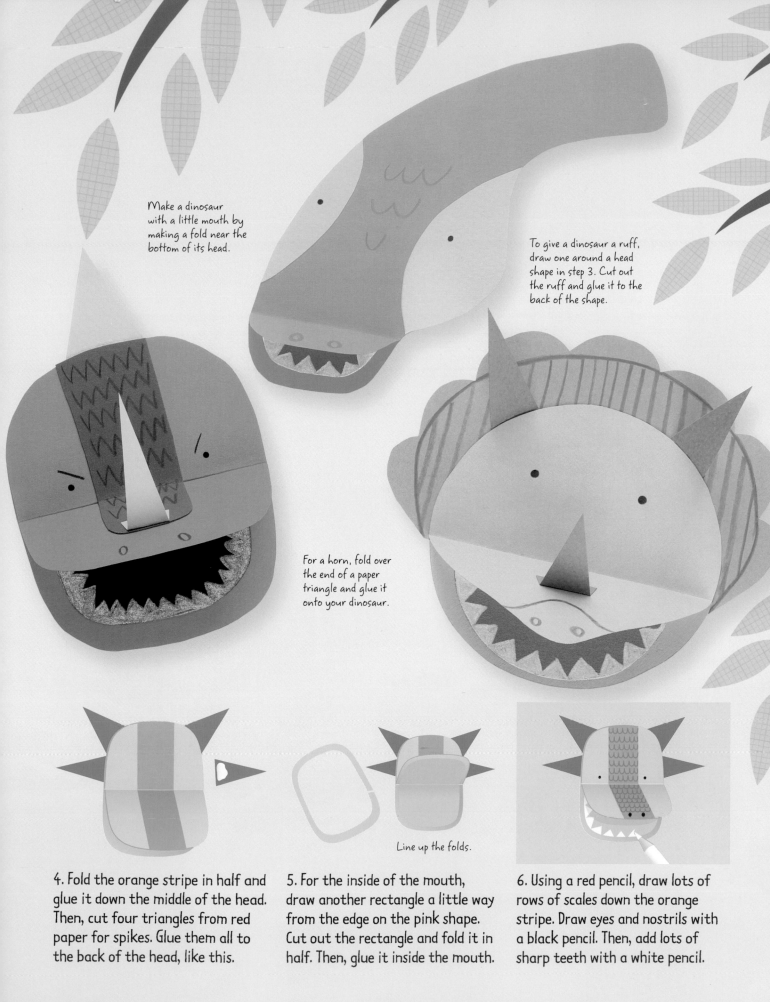

Make a dinosaur with a little mouth by making a fold near the bottom of its head.

To give a dinosaur a ruff, draw one around a head shape in step 3. Cut out the ruff and glue it to the back of the shape.

For a horn, fold over the end of a paper triangle and glue it onto your dinosaur.

Line up the folds.

4. Fold the orange stripe in half and glue it down the middle of the head. Then, cut four triangles from red paper for spikes. Glue them all to the back of the head, like this.

5. For the inside of the mouth, draw another rectangle a little way from the edge on the pink shape. Cut out the rectangle and fold it in half. Then, glue it inside the mouth.

6. Using a red pencil, draw lots of rows of scales down the orange stripe. Draw eyes and nostrils with a black pencil. Then, add lots of sharp teeth with a white pencil.

5

Swimming dinosaur painting

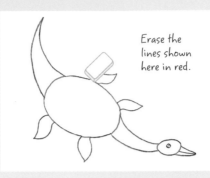

Erase the lines shown here in red.

The lines are shown here in yellow so that you can see them.

1. Use a pencil to draw a large oval for a dinosaur's body in the middle of a piece of thick white paper. Then, add four pointed shapes for its flippers, like this.

2. Draw an oval for a head, a little way from the body. Add pointed jaws, and an eye with a pupil. Then, draw a neck and a long tail. Erase the lines that join the shapes together.

3. Using a white wax crayon, draw a line of waves across the paper for the surface of the water. Add several shorter lines of waves, then draw little circles for bubbles.

You could do a large painting with several swimming dinosaurs. Draw their necks and tails at different angles.

The wax crayon will resist the paints.

4. Mix blue and green paints with water on an old plate, until they are really watery. Then, use a large paintbrush to paint lots of stripes across the paper for water.

5. Leave the paint to dry. Then, mix some more blue paint with a little water, to make it runny. Fill in the dinosaur with a thin paintbrush, but don't fill in the eye.

Lay your picture on an old newspaper.

6. To make water splashes, dip the brush into the paint again. Hold it over your picture and pull a finger back over the bristles to splatter the paper. Add lots more splashes.

Try drawing a dinosaur with an open mouth.

7. When all the paint is completely dry, use a dark blue pencil to draw an outline around the head, neck and tail. Add lots of short curving lines on the neck and tail, like this.

8. Fill in the eye with a yellow pencil. Then, use the blue pencil to draw around the eye and over the pupil. Add lots of sharp little teeth along the mouth, like this.

Stand-up stegosaurus

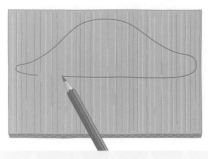

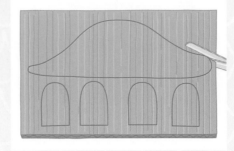

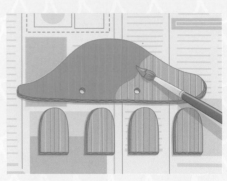

1. Lay a piece of corrugated cardboard on a table with the slots going down. Then, draw a long shape for the dinosaur's head, body and tail, like this.

2. Draw four arch shapes for the dinosaur's legs below the body. Then, carefully cut around all the shapes, trying not to bend the cardboard as you cut.

3. Make two holes near the bottom of the body with a hole puncher – these are for attaching the legs. Then, lay the shapes on newspaper, and paint them with thick paint.

To make a stegosaurus like this one, draw a shape with a curving neck and tail in step 1.

This stegosaurus has spines made from two kinds of material cut into different-sized diamond shapes.

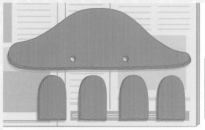

The strips need to be narrow enough to fit through the holes in the body.

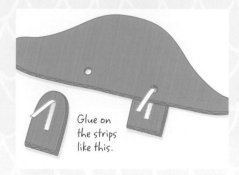

Glue on the strips like this.

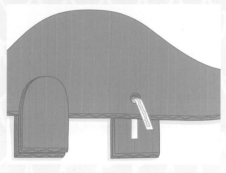

4. When the paint is dry, turn the shapes over and paint the other side. While the paint dries, cut two strips of thin cardboard, one and a half times the height of the legs.

5. Fold the cardboard strips in half. Spread glue on half of each strip and press it onto one of the legs. Slot the other half through one of the holes in the body.

6. Carefully spread glue on the top half of each cardboard strip. Then, press the other two legs onto the strips. Pull the legs gently so that they line up at the bottom.

You could make a tall dinosaur with a long neck.

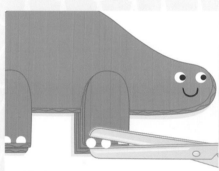

Leave the bottom off the hole puncher.

7. Take the bottom off a hole puncher and throw away any paper circles inside. Then, punch holes in a scrap of white paper to make lots of little paper circles.

8. Glue on two circles for eyes and draw black spots for pupils. Draw a smile, too. For toenails, glue circles onto the legs, overlapping the edge. Then, trim them, like this.

Spread out the spines.

9. For spines, cut diamond shapes from crêpe paper or material. Using the end of a toothpick, push the shapes into the slots in the cardboard along the dinosaur's back.

Hatching dinosaur eggs

You could use the egg white and yolk for cooking.

You don't need the top half of the eggshell.

1. Tap the middle of an egg sharply on the rim of a mug to crack it. Carefully break the egg in half with your fingers, over the mug. You don't need the egg white or yolk.

2. Wash the bottom half of the shell and leave it to dry. To make a baby dinosaur, cut a square of kitchen foil. Starting at the bottom edge, roll the foil into a sausage shape.

3. Bend the foil in half. With the fold at the top, squeeze the foil tightly to make a fatter shape. Then, fold the top end over two times to make the dinosaur's head.

These eggs were pressed onto blobs of poster tack to make them stand up. Be careful, though, not to use poster tack on any surface that it might damage.

The 'lids' on these eggs were made by covering the top half of the eggshells.

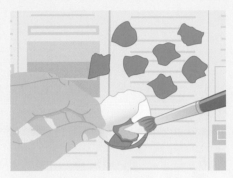

Hold the bottom of the dinosaur.

4. To cover the eggshell, tear lots of pieces from tissue paper. Brush part of the shell with thick white glue and press on tissue paper to cover it. Brush on more glue.

5. Then, add more pieces of tissue paper. Continue until the outside and inside of the shell are completely covered. Leave it on a piece of plastic foodwrap to dry.

6. To cover the dinosaur, tear lots of little pieces from another shade of tissue paper. Brush glue onto the dinosaur and press on pieces of tissue paper until it is covered.

Leave the glue to dry completely.

7. Let the dinosaur dry while you make the eyes. Cut two squares from white tissue paper. Spread glue on them, scrunch them into balls, then roll them in your fingers.

8. Roll each eye around in your hands until it is firm and round. Glue one eye onto each side of the head, like this. Then, leave the glue to dry completely.

9. Draw black spots on the eyes for pupils, then draw a mouth. Using white glue, glue a ball of poster tack into the egg. Press the bottom of the dinosaur onto the poster tack.

You could use stickers from the sticker pages to give your baby dinosaur spots or pointed teeth.

11

You could draw pterosaurs in the air, flying away from the volcano.

Dinosaur-world painting

Don't worry if you leave gaps as you scribble.

Add more runny paint if you need to.

1. Using a black wax crayon, draw two thick lines for the sides of a volcano. Then, to draw the crater and the top part of the volcano, scribble between the lines, like this.

2. Mix orange paint with water on an old plate until it is very runny. Then, use a large paintbrush to dab lots of paint into the volcano's crater to make a big blob.

3. For lava, hold a drinking straw a little way above the paint. Blow hard through the straw to 'chase' out trails of paint. Chase paint down the sides of the volcano, too.

Draw some plants, too.

4. Dip a thin paintbrush into the paint on the plate. Hold the brush over your picture and pull a finger back over the bristles to splatter the paper. Leave the paint to dry.

5. Fill in the volcano with black paint and add some ground next to it. Splatter on more black paint for flying ash. Then, when the paint is dry, add dinosaurs with a black pen.

Look at this picture for ideas of dinosaurs and plants you could draw.

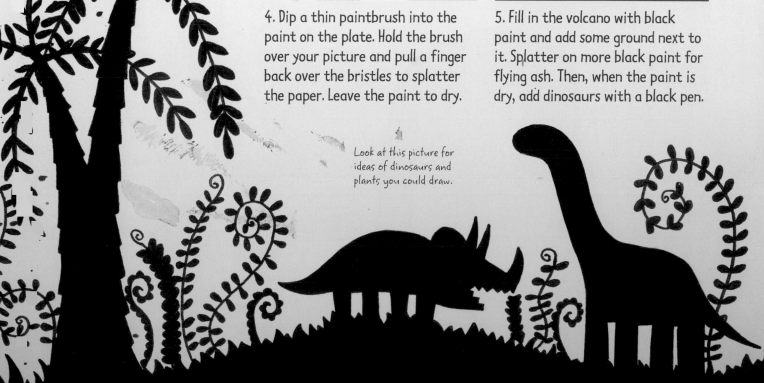

3-D dinosaur

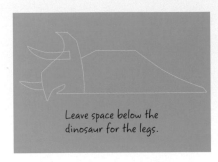

Leave space below the dinosaur for the legs.

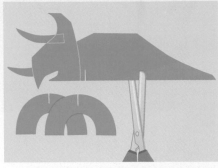

1. Draw a pointed shape for a dinosaur's head on a piece of thin cardboard. Add a long shape for the body and tail. Then, add two horns on the head, like this.

2. Draw two big arches for legs, making them about the same height as the dinosaur's back. Then, carefully cut around the tail, body and head, and cut out the legs, too.

3. Cut a narrow slot into the top of each leg, cutting halfway down into the leg. Then, cut two slots the same length into the bottom of the body, like this.

Try making a dinosaur with a big sail on its back, like this.

Lay the pieces on an old newspaper.

4. Cut a white paper circle for an eye. Glue it on and add a dot for a pupil. Use a felt-tip pen to draw outlines on the dinosaur and its legs, then erase any pencil lines.

5. Using another felt-tip pen, draw toenails and add lots of spots. Then, to make the dinosaur stand up, slide the slots in the legs and body together, like this.

To help a tall dinosaur stand up, make the slot for its legs near the front of its body.

You could add spikes on the tail.

15

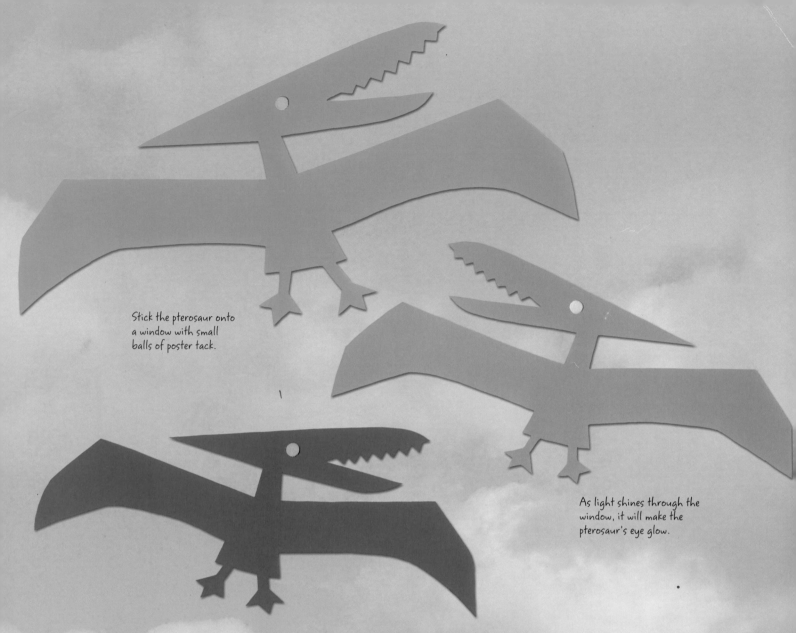

Stick the pterosaur onto a window with small balls of poster tack.

As light shines through the window, it will make the pterosaur's eye glow.

Glowing-eyed pterosaur

Make the head overlap the body.

1. Draw a triangle for a pterosaur's body on thick paper. Add a sideways triangle for a head, then draw a toothy mouth inside it. Draw two big wings and two little legs.

2. Carefully cut out the pterosaur. To make an eye, slide one corner of a hole puncher over the head. Move it until one end is over the middle of the head, then punch a hole.

3. To make a 'glowing' eye, cut a small piece of bright tissue paper. Spread some glue around the eye hole and press on the tissue paper. Then, turn the pterosaur over.

Dinosaur drawings

1. Using a pencil, draw the outline of one of the dinosaurs on this page on white paper. Draw over the line with a black felt-tip pen, then add a dot for an eye.

2. To add shadows, draw lots of short lines down the left-hand side of the legs. Then, add more shadows along the underside of the neck, tummy and tail, like this.

3. Add patterns on the dinosaur with bright felt-tip pens. Draw a mixture of stripes, loops, spots and zigzags – look at the dinosaurs on this page for ideas.

Nigersaurus

Ouranosaurus

Diplodocus

Triceratops

Stegosaurus

Tyrannosaurus

Brachiosaurus

Coelophysis

Dacentrurus

Apatosaurus

17

Big Rex picture

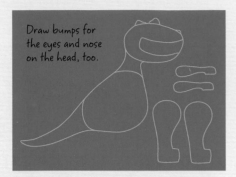

Draw bumps for the eyes and nose on the head, too.

1. Draw shapes for the dinosaur's head and body on thick paper. Add a neck and a tail, then draw a big mouth. Draw two arms and two big legs, then cut out all the shapes.

2. Erase any pencil lines. Then, draw two shapes for eyes on white paper. Cut them out and glue them onto the head. Add dots for pupils and nostrils with a black felt-tip pen.

Snip with the tips of your scissors.

3. Cut two strips of white paper for teeth. Glue them to the back of the head, overlapping the dinosaur's jaws. Then, turn the dinosaur over and snip triangles for teeth.

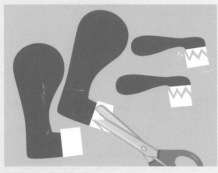

4. To make claws, cut four small white paper rectangles. Glue one rectangle over the end of each arm and each leg. Then, cut zigzags for claws, like this.

Glue on the scales in rows, starting at the bottom.

5. For scales, fold several pieces of paper in half, then in half again. Draw circles and cut them out. Glue the scales onto the belly, then trim any that overlap the edge.

The cardboard squares will make the top arm and leg stand out a little.

6. Glue an arm and a leg onto the back of the body. Cut two small cardboard squares and glue them on the back of the other arm and leg. Then, glue them onto the body, too.

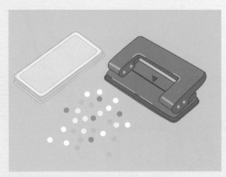

7. For little scales on the dinosaur's tail and leg, take the bottom off a hole puncher. Throw away any paper circles inside, then leave the bottom off the hole puncher.

8. Punch holes in scraps of paper until you have lots of little circles. Then, glue the paper circles onto the dinosaur's tail and the top of the leg, like this.

You could make a tree covered with brown scales, too.

To make a plant, cut little paper circles in half for leaves and glue them along a stem.

Swampy painting

Draw squiggles for the edge of the swamp.

1. Draw an oval for a dinosaur's body on white paper. Add its head, neck, legs, tail and face. Then, draw the edge of a swampy pool and add another dinosaur swimming in it.

2. Draw lots of plants, tree trunks and pond weed. Mix some yellow paint with water on an old plate until it is really watery. Then, brush the paint all over the paper.

3. While the paint is wet, brush watery brown and green paints on the trees and plants. Brush watery paints on the ground and the pool, too. Leave the paint to dry.

You could add other dinosaurs to your painting, too – look at the ones in this picture for ideas.

4. Mix yellow, orange, pink and red paints with water to make them runny. Fill in the dinosaurs, then dab on spots of darker paint while the paint is still wet.

5. When the paint is completely dry, draw over the outlines with a brown pen. Leave some of the trees and plants without outlines, to make them look far away.

Draw a baby dinosaur in exactly the same way as the dinosaur in the steps – just draw smaller shapes.

You could add some dragonflies flying above the swamp.

To add a dinosaur's reflection, dab patches of the same shade of paint below it.

Draw a little oval with curved lines around it for ripples in the water.

Try adding painted patches like these under the dinosaurs for shadows.

21

Flying pterosaur

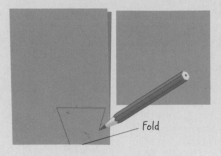

Fold

1. Cut a very long rectangle from thick paper. Cut out a square, too. Fold the rectangle in half, short ends together. Draw a shape for the pterosaur's body against the fold.

You could decorate your pterosaur with a silver pen, or use stickers from the sticker pages.

2. Add a pointed wing shape above the body, like this. Draw a leg with claws against the fold, too. Then, draw a pointed head and neck on the paper square.

Don't cut along the folds.

3. Holding the layers of paper together, cut out the body and wing shape. Carefully cut around the leg and claws, too. Then, cut out the head and neck.

4. Fold the top wing down along the pencil line, like this. Press the fold down well, then turn the paper over. Fold down the other wing in the same way, lining up the edges.

Line up the neck with the front edge of the body.

5. Open out the shape again. Turn the head over to the back and spread glue on the bottom of the neck. Then, turn the head over again and press it onto the body.

6. Spread glue on the folded end of the legs and press them on, too. Then, cut a piece of thread or yarn to hang the pterosaur from. Tape it halfway down the body.

7. Spread glue as far as the fold line on one half of the body, like this. Then, press both halves of the body together. Hold them firmly until the glue sticks.

The spots on this paper were printed using bubblewrap – see steps 3-5 on pages 30-31.

You could decorate the head and legs before making your pterosaur.

8. Draw a black dot on each side of the head for the eyes. Separate the legs by bending them out a little. Then, fold down the wings and hang the pterosaur using the thread.

Spiky dinosaur collage

Don't worry if some pieces go over the edge of the oval.

You don't need this piece.

1. For the dinosaur's body, cut a large oval from white paper. Lay it on an old newspaper. Then, rip lots of pieces from old newspaper pages. Glue them all over the oval.

2. Cut three thick strips from magazine pictures and glue them onto the body. Trim any pieces of paper that overlap the edge. Glue the body onto a large piece of paper.

3. For the head, cut two rounded rectangles, one a little bigger than the other. Cut a zigzag across the bottom of the bigger rectangle, then glue it onto the smaller one.

Choose magazine pictures with interesting textures and patterns to decorate your dinosaur.

4. Cut four triangles for spikes and glue them to the back of the head. Cut a paper circle and half circle for an eye. Glue them onto the head, then draw a black spot for a pupil.

You could make a volcano with clouds of smoke and runny lava from magazine paper shapes, too.

5. Glue the head onto the body. Then, draw a curved tail and four legs on magazine pictures. Cut out all the shapes and glue them onto your picture.

Cut leaf shapes from paper and glue them together for plants.

6. Cut out lots of paper triangles for spikes. Glue a line of them along the dinosaur's back. Then, glue more spikes all over the body and along the tail. Leave the glue to dry.

Spotted dinosaur drawing

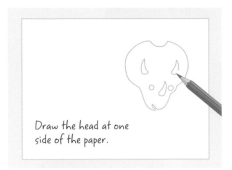

Draw the head at one side of the paper.

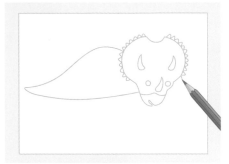

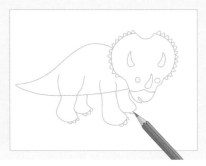

1. For a dinosaur's head, draw a shape like this on a piece of white paper. Add circles for eyes, with a horn between them. Then, draw two more horns above the eyes.

2. Draw a long pointed shape for the body and tail. Then, add a line across the dinosaur's nose. Draw lots of little triangles around the top of the head for a bony frill.

3. Draw two legs, overlapping the dinosaur's tummy. Then, add the other back and front leg, making them slighter shorter than the other legs. Draw claws on the feet.

Try drawing a dinosaur with lots of spines, and bright spots and rings on its head and tummy.

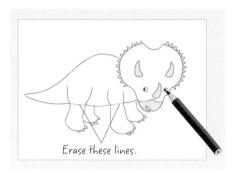

Erase these lines.

Press lightly as you fill in the gaps.

4. Using a red pencil, draw over the outlines. Then, fill in the bony frill, horns, chin and claws with a yellow pencil. Draw little black spots in the eyes for pupils.

5. Draw orange spots on the head, then add rings around them. Draw smaller yellow and orange spots between the rings. Fill in the gaps with an orange or yellow pencil.

6. Draw big orange spots on the body, then add yellow and paler orange rings around them. Pressing lightly with an orange pencil, fill in the gaps between the rings.

You could draw a big dinosaur and decorate its back with lots of green spots.

Sitting dinosaur card

Keep the fold on the left.

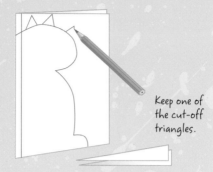

Keep one of the cut-off triangles.

Don't draw any spikes at this end.

1. Fold a rectangle of thick white paper in half. Then, starting at the bottom of the fold, draw a diagonal line. Draw a line down the left-hand side of the card, too.

2. Holding the layers together, cut along the diagonal line. Then, draw curves for the head and belly, and a foot below the belly. Add a few spikes on the head, too.

3. Cut out the dinosaur, through both layers. Don't cut down the fold. For a tail, draw a diagonal line on one of the triangles from step 2. Add little spikes along the top.

If you're going to send the card, carefully fold back the tail to fit it into an envelope.

To make a dinosaur like this, turn the card so that the fold is at the top, then draw the dinosaur.

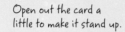
Cut here.

4. Cut around the tail and spikes. Glue the end of the tail to the back of the card. Then, make a cut from the top of the tail to the pencil line, along the red line shown here.

5. Then, starting at the cut you made in step 4, cut lots of little triangles along the fold to make spikes. Carefully erase any remaining pencil lines.

6. Lay the dinosaur on an old newspaper. Mix some orange paint with some water on an old plate, to make it runny. Then, brush the paint all over the dinosaur.

Open out the card a little to make it stand up.

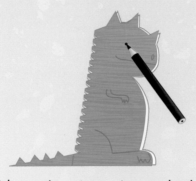

7. Leave the paint to dry completely. Then, use an orange pencil to draw an arm, a leg and a foot. Draw a mouth and a nostril, then add a black dot for an eye.

Use different fingers to make different-sized spots.

8. Pour more orange paint onto the plate, but don't add any water this time. Fill in the dinosaur's spikes with a thin paintbrush. Then, use a fingertip to print some spots.

You could cut only a few triangles into the fold on the dinosaur's back.

9. Pour some thick white paint onto an old plate, then use the tip of a thin paintbrush to paint three little pointed teeth. Leave the paint to dry completely.

Printed dinosaur

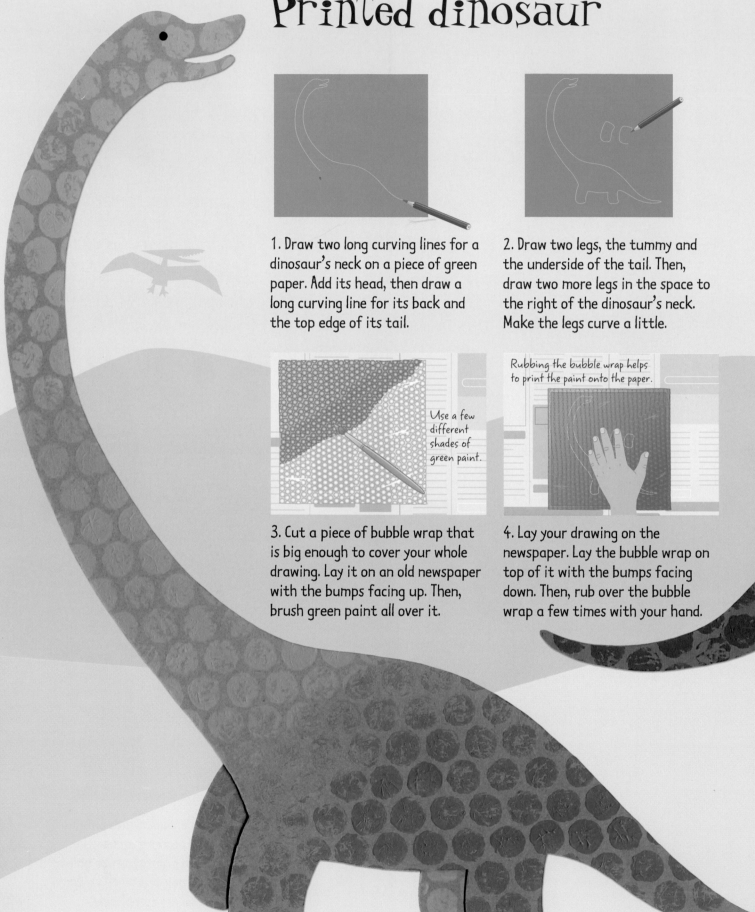

1. Draw two long curving lines for a dinosaur's neck on a piece of green paper. Add its head, then draw a long curving line for its back and the top edge of its tail.

2. Draw two legs, the tummy and the underside of the tail. Then, draw two more legs in the space to the right of the dinosaur's neck. Make the legs curve a little.

Use a few different shades of green paint.

3. Cut a piece of bubble wrap that is big enough to cover your whole drawing. Lay it on an old newspaper with the bumps facing up. Then, brush green paint all over it.

Rubbing the bubble wrap helps to print the paint onto the paper.

4. Lay your drawing on the newspaper. Lay the bubble wrap on top of it with the bumps facing down. Then, rub over the bubble wrap a few times with your hand.

You could make several dinosaurs using different shades of green paper and paint.

5. Carefully remove the bubble wrap, by lifting up a corner and peeling it away from the paper. Try not to smudge the paint. Then, leave the paint to dry completely.

6. When the paint is dry, carefully cut around the dinosaur. Cut out the extra legs, too. Then, draw a dot for the dinosaur's eye with a black pencil.

7. Turn the dinosaur over. Spread glue along the right-hand edge of the legs and a little way up onto the body. Then, turn the two extra legs over and press them on.

Moonlit T. rex silhouette

The patches of chalk are for shadows on the moon.

Smudge the chalk out from the circle.

Erase any pencil lines before you glue the dinosaur on.

1. For the moon, draw around a small plate on cream paper. Cut out the circle. Then, rub a chalk pastel on the end of one of your fingers. Rub patches of chalk on the moon.

2. Using a pencil, draw around the plate on black paper. Lift off the plate, then draw a thick line over the circle with a white chalk. Smudge the edge for a 'glow'.

3. Glue the moon inside the 'glow'. Then, draw a T. rex's head and body on black paper. Add teeth and arms. Cut it out and glue it onto the paper, overlapping the moon.

Photographic manipulation by John Russell
This edition first published in 2012 by Usborne Publishing Ltd., Usborne House, 83-85 Saffron Hill, London, England. www.usborne.com